How beautiful on the mountains are the feet of one who brings good news, who heralds peace, proclaims salvation...
(Isaiah 52:7)

The most beautiful Christmas Story

According to the Gospels of St Luke and St Matthew

Illustrated by Marie Poirier

CTS Children's Books

Maïte Roche

The most
beautiful
Christmas Story

God sent the Angel Gabriel
to announce news of great
joy to a young girl from
Nazareth called Mary.

Nazareth was a little village in Galilee where Mary lived with her family. Ever since she was a little girl Mary had loved God with her whole heart, and she had waited with hope for the coming of the Saviour who would bring joy to the world.

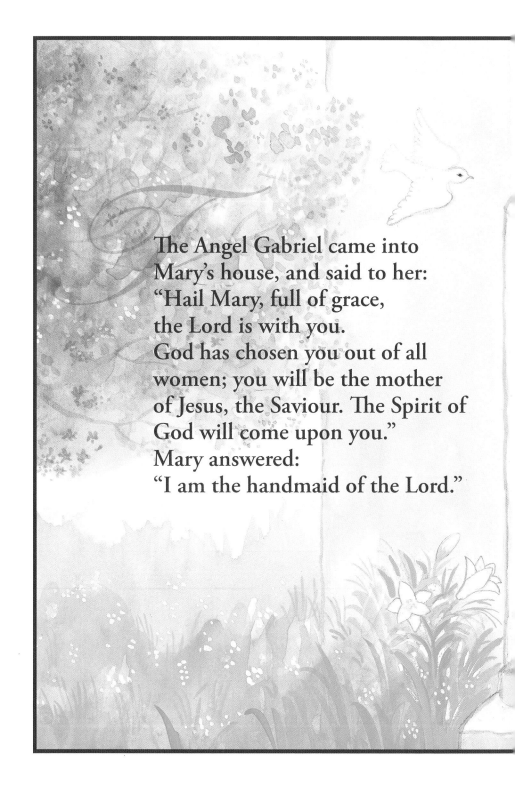

The Angel Gabriel came into
Mary's house, and said to her:
"Hail Mary, full of grace,
the Lord is with you.
God has chosen you out of all
women; you will be the mother
of Jesus, the Saviour. The Spirit of
God will come upon you."
Mary answered:
"I am the handmaid of the Lord."

Joseph was engaged to Mary.
He was the village carpenter.
While he was resting after his
work, the Angel Gabriel
appeared to him in a dream,
and said: "Listen, Joseph:
Mary is expecting a baby,
who comes from God.
You will give him the
name Jesus.
He is to be the Saviour."

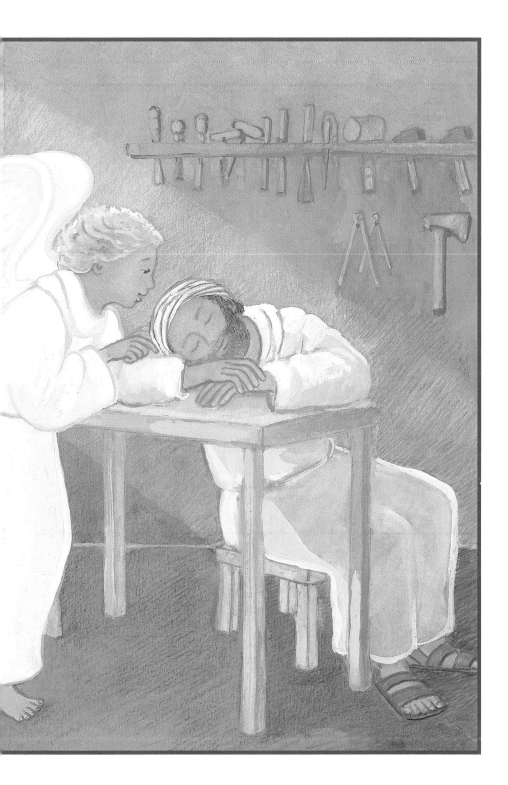

Quickly, Joseph ran to Mary's house.
He was so happy! He now knew
that God had chosen him to love
and protect Mary and Jesus.
How wonderful!

It was the day of Joseph and Mary's wedding. Their families and friends all arrived.

"Come and sing and
dance with us!"

The Emperor Caesar Augustus ordered all the people who lived in his empire to be counted. Joseph had to go and give his name at Bethlehem in Judaea, the town where he had been born. It was winter, and the weather was cold. A little donkey carried Mary. She was thinking about Jesus, who would soon be born.

When Joseph and Mary arrived in Bethlehem there was no room left for them at the inn. Someone showed them a cave a little further on which was used as a stable for farm animals.

In the middle of the night, Mary brought her little baby into the world. She wrapped him tenderly in swaddling-clothes. Joseph said softly: "Jesus, you've only got a manger for your cradle, and a poor stable for your house, but our hearts are full of love for you, the Son that God has given us."

Out in the countryside, some shepherds were watching over their sheep.
Suddenly, a great light shone down on them, and they were frightened.
The angel of the Lord appeared to them and said: "Don't be afraid!

I bring you joyful news. A Saviour has been born for you! He is a little baby and you will find him in a manger, in Bethlehem."

"Quick! Let's go and see this
little baby who has just been born!"
The shepherds ran to the crib
and in the sky lots of angels
sang for joy:
"Glory to God in the highest!
Peace to men all over the earth!"
Heaven and earth were celebrating.
It was Christmas night.

The shepherds arrived at the stable.
"An angel has told us that the Saviour
has just been born!"

"He is called Jesus," said Joseph.
Then the shepherds gazed at Jesus and their
hearts were filled with peace and joy.

The shepherds went back singing
about the glory of God:
"Rejoice! The Saviour has been
born, and we have seen him!"
Everyone who heard them was
astonished. Mary treasured
all these memories in her heart.

In a far-off country in the East, some Magi saw a new star shining: "This is a sign that a great king has just been born. Its light is shining on us. Let's go and pay him homage."

The Magi arrived at Jerusalem,
in the palace of King Herod.
They asked: "Where is the king
who has just been born?"

The learned men answered that he would be born in Bethlehem. Herod was afraid. He did not want there to be any king except himself!

He pretended to the Magi that he wanted to go and worship Jesus too.

"Go and find this king, and then come and tell me where he is."

In Bethlehem, the Magi were filled with joy.
They knelt down to worship Jesus
and they offered him precious
gifts: gold, frankincense
and myrrh.

The angel of the Lord warned the Magi
not to go back to Herod.
They went back home by another road.
Herod was furious about Jesus.
He shouted to his soldiers:
"Go to Bethlehem, kill that baby,
and any others that might be him!"

During the night, the Angel Gabriel warned Joseph in a dream: "Get up, set off quickly with Mary, for Herod wants to harm the baby."

Joseph led the little donkey
that was carrying Mary and Jesus.
Herod's soldiers were looking
for them in the night.
"Don't worry, God is with us,"
said Mary. Jesus slept peacefully
in his mother's arms.

Joseph, Mary and Jesus arrived in Egypt.
Herod could no longer hurt them.
"Blessed be the Lord who has saved us!"

Some time later, the Angel Gabriel told Joseph: "Herod is dead, the danger is over." Joseph, Mary and Jesus went back to Nazareth. Their family and friends came to welcome them. They were so happy to be all together again!

Some time later, the Angel Gabriel told Joseph: "Herod is dead, the danger is over." Joseph, Mary and Jesus went back to Nazareth. Their family and friends came to welcome them. They were so happy to be all together again!

In Nazareth, Jesus grew up with his family. The Spirit of God was with him. Mary told him tenderly: "Jesus, you fill us with joy and you show us that happiness means having a heart full of love."

The Bible for little children, *by Maïte Roche*

(ISBN 1 86082 399 8 CTS Code CH 2)

The Gospel for little children, *by Maïte Roche*

(ISBN 1 86082 400 5 CTS Code CH 1)

The Rosary, *by Juliette Levivier*

(ISBN 1 86082 397 1 CTS Code CH 3)

The Way of the Cross, *by Juliette Levivier*

(ISBN 1 86082 398 X CTS Code CH 4)

First prayers for little children, *by Maïte Roche*

(ISBN 978 1 86082 443 2 CTS Code CH 5)

Praying with the friends of Jesus, *by Juliette Levivier*

(ISBN 978 1 86082 444 9 CTS Code CH 6)

Prayers around the Crib, *by Juliette Levivier*

(ISBN 978 1 86082 445 6 CTS Code CH 7)

The most beautiful Christmas Story, *by Maïte Roche*

(ISBN 978 1 86082 446 3 CTS Code CH 8)

Faith for children, *by Christine Pedotti*

(ISBN 978 1 86082 447 0 CTS Code CH 9)

The most beautiful Christmas Story: Published 2007 by the Incorporated Catholic Truth Society, 40-46 Harleyford Road, London SE11 5AY. Tel: 020 7640 0042; Fax: 020 7640 0046; www.cts-online.org.uk. Copyright © 2007 The Incorporated Catholic Truth Society in this English-language edition.

ISBN: 978 1 86082 446 3   CTS Code CH 8

La plus belle histoire de Noël written and illustrated by Maïte Roche, published 2005 by Edifa-Mame, 15-27 rue Moussorgski, 75018 Paris; ISBN Mame 2-7289-1161-4; Edifa 2-9145-8071-1; Copyright © Groupe Fleurus 2005.